Phonics Success

Louis Fidge and Christine Moorcroft

Contents

4–5   Introduction

Letters of the alphabet

6–7   The alphabet a-i
8–9   The alphabet j-r
10–11   The alphabet s-z
12–13   Upper- and lower-case letter matching

Initial letters of words

14   Letters and sounds s, t, p, n
15   Letters and sounds m, d, g, c
16   Letters and sounds k, r, h, b
17   Letters and sounds l, f, a, e

Middle letters of words

18–19   a in the middle
20–21   e in the middle
22–23   i in the middle
24–25   o in the middle
26–27   u in the middle

Letters of the alphabet

28–29   The alphabet

Two consonants – one sound

30   Words ending –ck
31   Words ending –ff
32   Words ending –ll
33   Words ending –ss
34–35   Words beginning ch–
36–37   Words beginning sh–
38   Words ending –sh
39   Words with sh
40–41   Words with th
42–43   Words ending –ng

Consonant beginnings and endings

44–45   Letter j
46–47   Letter v

Contents

48–49   Letter w

50–51   Letter x

52–53   Letter y

54   Words beginning z

55   Words ending zz

56–57   Words beginning qu

Letters of the alphabet

58–59   Alphabetical order

Two vowels – one sound

60   Words with ee

61   Words with ai

62   Words with oo

63   Words with oa

64–65   Words with ar

66–67   Words with or

68–69   Words with ur

70–71   Words with ow

72–73   Words with oi

74–75   Words with er

Three vowels – one sound

76–77   Words with ear

78   Words with air

79   Words with ure

80–81   Words with igh

Consonant blends

82–83   Words with s + consonant t

84–85   Words beginning s + consonant

86–87   Words beginning consonant + l

88–89   Words beginning consonant + r

90–91   Words ending l + consonant

92–93   Words ending n + consonant

What have I learned?

94–96   What have I learned?

Introduction

What is phonics?
Phonics is the relationship between sounds (phonemes) and letters or groups of letters (graphemes). Learning phonics involves listening to sounds, recognising sounds and discriminating between sounds as well as learning how sounds are represented by letters.

Phonics in the Foundation Stage (Ages 3 to 5)
Children aged 4 to 5 follow the Foundation Stage curriculum, in which literacy includes reading and writing. Phonics is important in both of these. Literacy is linked with communication and language, which includes listening and being attentive, understanding and speaking. By the age of 5, children are expected to use phonic knowledge to write words in ways that match their spoken sounds, plus some irregular common words such as 'have', 'the', 'they', 'was', 'all' and simple sentences that they and others can read. They are also expected to spell some words correctly and others in a way that makes use of phonics but might include incorrect choices: for example, 'chays' for 'chase', 'muny' for 'money'.

When first learning phonics, children should have many opportunities to enjoy listening to and reading stories, poems, songs and rhymes, as well as information books about topics that interest them.

Phonics Practice Activities 1 is based on current practice in schools and presents letters and sounds in ways that should be familiar to children from their school work.

This book helps children to learn the relationship between sounds and letters. They learn to:
- distinguish one sound from another
- recognise, distinguish and write the letters of the alphabet
- link sounds to letters, naming as well as sounding the letters of the alphabet
- hear and say the initial sound in words and know which letters represent some of the sounds
- hear and say sounds in words in the order in which they occur
- recognize and practise correct letter formation and handwriting.

How this book is organised
Letters of the alphabet (p. 6–13) introduces upper- and lower-case letters, in order, by name. You could use these terms with your child or 'capital letters' and 'lower-case letters' (as there is no other simple term for 'lower-case'). The letters are introduced in a way that helps children learn letter formation as well as position in the alphabet.

There are further activities on the letters of the alphabet at later stages of the book (p. 28–29, 58–59).

Initial letters of words introduces the sounds the letters represent in very short words in a similar order to that used in most schools. The most common sound is introduced for each letter. Most children notice the first sound of a word more easily that the others. Alternative sounds for each letter come later.

Middle sounds focuses on the middle vowel sound (a, e, i, o, u) of three-letter words that begin and end with a consonant. The activities use the most common sound for each vowel, i.e. the short vowel sounds 'a' as in cat, 'e' as in get, 'i' as in pin, 'o' as in hot and 'u' as in cup. Alternative sounds for these letters come later.

Two consonants – one sound introduces pairs of consonants that together stand for a single sound: 'ck' as in sock, 'ff' as in cuff, 'll' as in tell, 'ch' as in chop, 'sh' as in ship or fish, 'th' as in the, moth, path and with, and 'ng' at the end of words like sing. (Note that ng is not separated into n-g.) Other ch sounds come later. It is helpful to use the term 'two letters one sound' with children, so that they know that they should sound the two letters as one, rather than separately.

Consonant beginnings and endings introduces the more difficult and less commonly used consonants, some of which do not occur at the beginning of words: j, v, w, x, y, z. It also introduces zz and qu, since zz is more common than z at the ends of words and q is not used alone in English words.

Two vowels – one sound introduces some vowel sounds that are represented by two letters: ee, ai, oo, oa, ar, or, ur, ow, oi, er. Only one vowel sound (the simplest or most common) is used for each. Other vowel sounds for these pairs of letters come later – as do other ways of spelling the same vowel sounds.

Three vowels – one sound introduces vowel sounds represented by three letters: ear, ure, igh. Only one vowel sound (the simplest or most common) is used for each. Other vowel sounds for these sets of letters come later, as do other ways of spelling the same vowel sounds.

Consonant blends are groups of consonants that are sounded separately in a word and then blended to spell or say the word. The consonant s is used in this way in many words: for example, st, sn, sw, sk, sp, sn, sl. Other blended consonants introduced here are bl, fl, pl, cl, pr, br, tr, gr dr, cr, and, at the ends of words lt, lk, lm, lb, lf, lk, lp, nd, nt, nk

What have I learned?
This section provides activities to help you and your child assess what has been learned. It helps you to determine what other practice your child needs. Consult your child's teacher if you have any concerns.

The alphabet a-d

Letters a-d

Write the letters.

Say the names of the letters.

Colour them on the alphabet ladder.

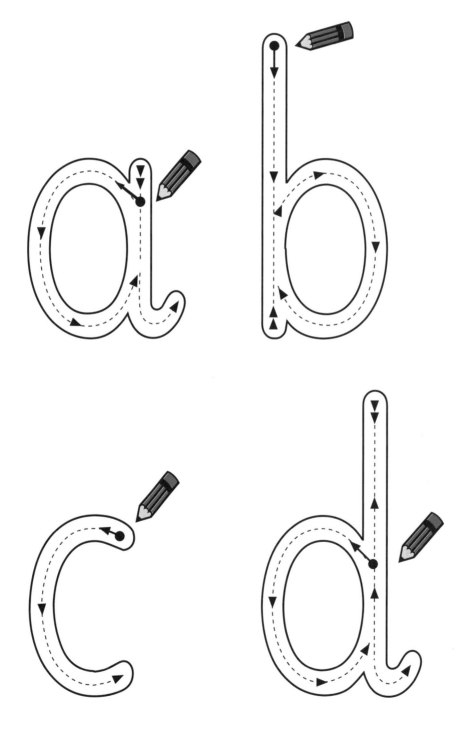

A a
B b
C c
D d
E e
F f
G g
H h
I i
J j
K k
L l
M m
N n
O o
P p
Q q
R r
S s
T t
U u
V v
W w
X x
Y y
Z z

Letters e-i

Write the letters.

Say the names of the letters.

Colour them on the alphabet ladder.

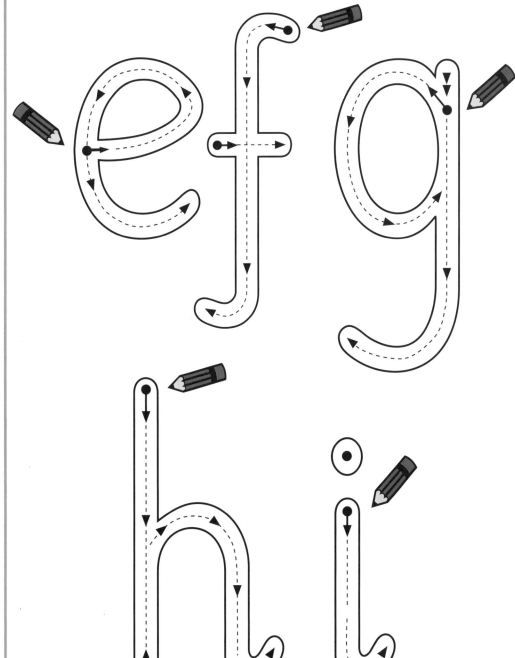

A a
B b
C c
D d
E e
F f
G g
H h
I i
J j
K k
L l
M m
N n
O o
P p
Q q
R r
S s
T t
U u
V v
W w
X x
Y y
Z z

The alphabet j–n

Letters j–n

Write the letters.

Say the names of the letters.

Colour them on the alphabet ladder.

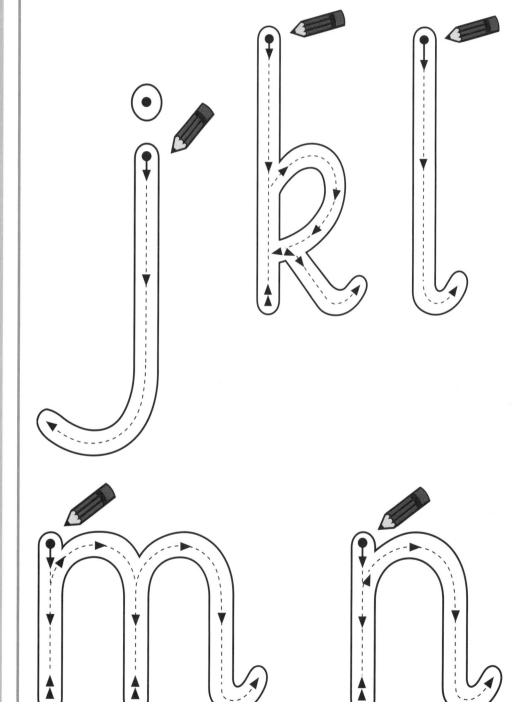

A a
B b
C c
D d
E e
F f
G g
H h
I i
J j
K k
L l
M m
N n
O o
P p
Q q
R r
S s
T t
U u
V v
W w
X x
Y y
Z z

Letters o–r

Write the letters.

Say the names of the letters.

Colour them on the alphabet ladder.

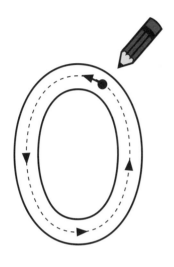

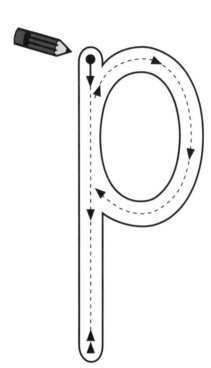

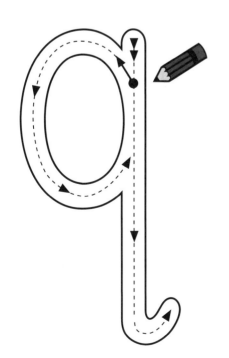

A a
B b
C c
D d
E e
F f
G g
H h
I i
J j
K k
L l
M m
N n
O o
P p
Q q
R r
S s
T t
U u
V v
W w
X x
Y y
Z z

The alphabet s-v

Letters s-v

Write the letters.

Say the names of the letters.

Colour them on the alphabet ladder.

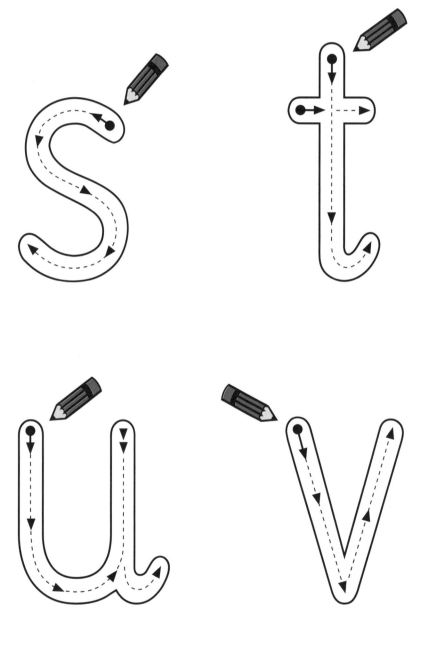

A	a
B	b
C	c
D	d
E	e
F	f
G	g
H	h
I	i
J	j
K	k
L	l
M	m
N	n
O	o
P	p
Q	q
R	r
S	s
T	t
U	u
V	v
W	w
X	x
Y	y
Z	z

Letters w–z

Write the letters.

Say the names of the letters.

Colour them on the alphabet ladder.

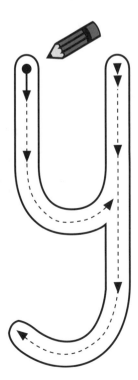

A a
B b
C c
D d
E e
F f
G g
H h
I i
J j
K k
L l
M m
N n
O o
P p
Q q
R r
S s
T t
U u
V v
W w
X x
Y y
Z z

Upper- and lower-case letter matching

Matching letters a–m

Match each rocket to its planet.

Parent's tip — Use the names of the letters, not the sounds they represent. If your child still has difficulty recognising the letters, provide plasticine or modelling clay and help him/her to make some upper- and lower-case letters to match (beginning with the first four).

Upper- and lower-case letter matching

Matching letters n–z

Park each van in its correct place.

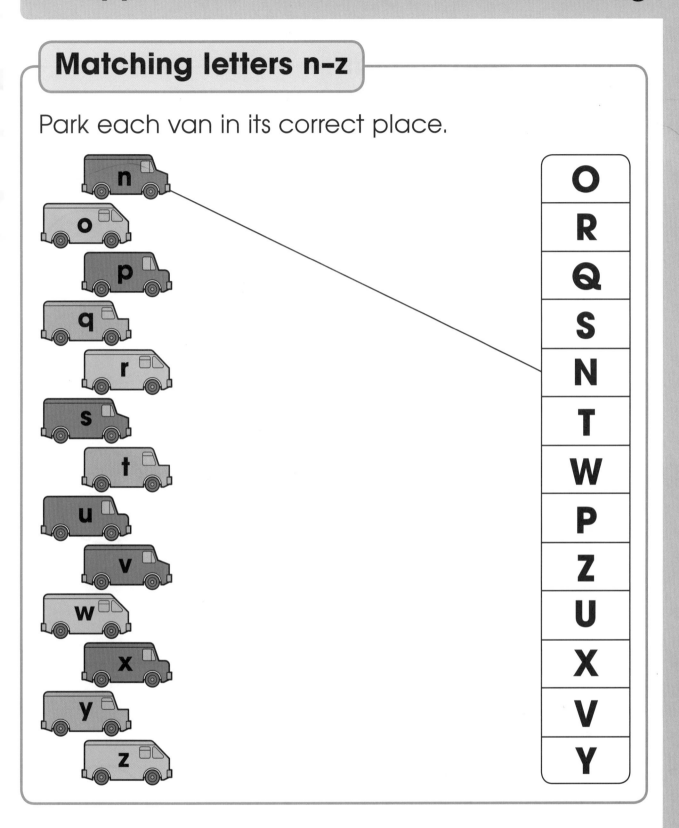

Letters and sounds s, t, p, n

Letters and sounds

What's in the box?
Say the words.
Write the first letter
of each word.

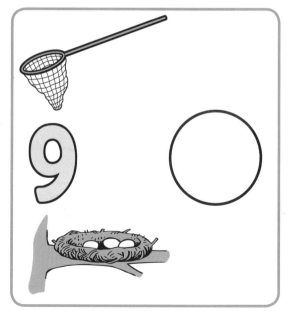

Letters and sounds

What's in the box?
Say the words.
Write the first letter
of each word.

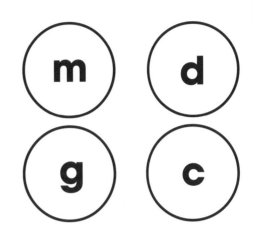

Letters and sounds k, r, h, b

Letters and sounds

What's in the box?
Say the words.
Write the first letter
of each word.

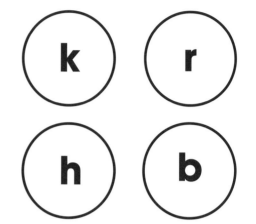

Letters and sounds

What's in the box?
Say the words.
Write the first letter
of each word.

l   f

a   e

EXIT

a in the middle

a m**a**n in a v**a**n with a f**a**n

a words

Say the words.

Write the letters for the sounds. Write the words.

 | m | a | n |

 | | | |

 | | | |

Write another rhyming word.

| | a | n |

Rhyming words

Say some words that rhyme with **cat**.
Write the letters for the sounds. Write the words.

c | a | t

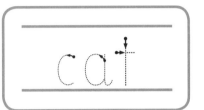

cat

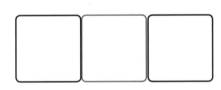

Make up a rhyme about a cat. Draw a picture.

e in the middle

Read the rhyme

ten men and a hen

e words

Say the words.

Write the letters for the sounds. Write the words.

| m | e | n |

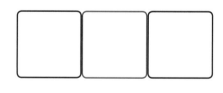

Write another rhyming word.

| | e | n |

Rhyming words

Say some words that rhyme with **wet**.
Write the letters for the sounds. Write the words.

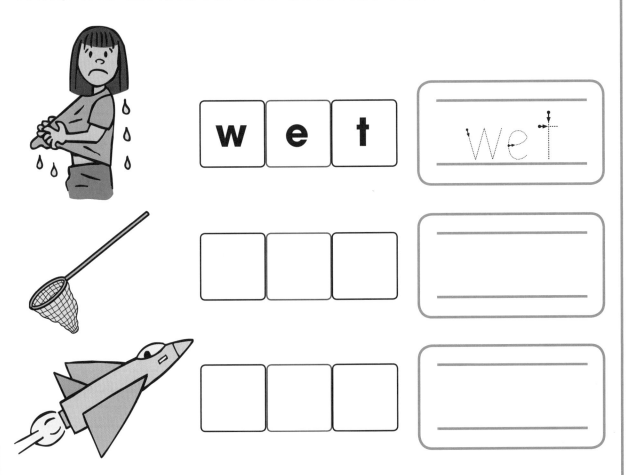

| w | e | t |

Make up a rhyme about a jet. Draw a picture.

i in the middle

Read the rhymes

a p**in** in a t**in**

a t**in** in a b**in**

i words

Say the words.

Write the letters for the sounds. Write the words.

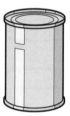

t	i	n

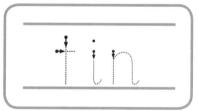

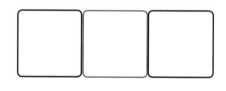

Write another rhyming word.

Rhyming words

Say some words that rhyme with **big**.

Write the letters for the sounds. Write the words.

b	i	g

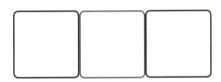

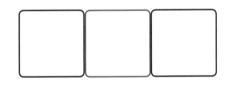

Make up a rhyme about something big.

Draw a picture.

o in the middle

Read the rhyme

a d**o**g on a l**o**g in a f**o**g

o words

Say the words.

Write the letters for the sounds. Write the words.

 | f | o | g | | *fog* |

 | | | | | |

 | | | | | |

Write another rhyming word.

 | | o | g | | |

Rhyming words

Say some words that rhyme with **hop**.

Write the letters for the sounds. Write the words.

Make up a rhyme about something that goes pop. Draw a picture.

u in the middle

Read the rhymes

a b**u**g in a m**u**g   a b**u**g in a j**u**g

u words

Say the words.

Write the letters for the sounds. Write the words.

b	u	g

Write another rhyming word.

	u	g

Rhyming words

Say some words that rhyme with **rub**.

Write the letters for the sounds. Write the words.

r	u	b

rub

Make up a rhyme about a cub. Draw a picture.

The alphabet

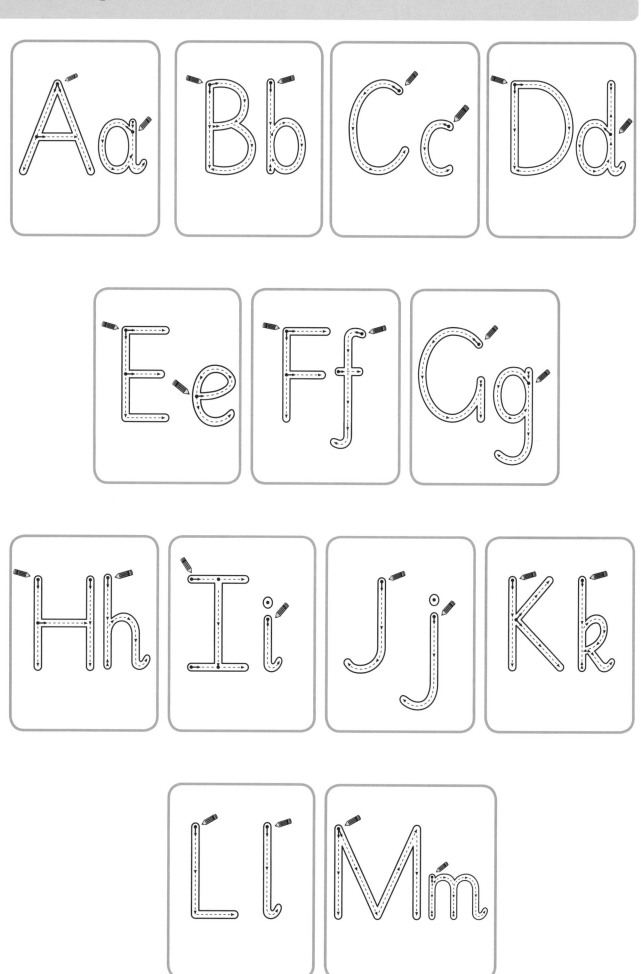

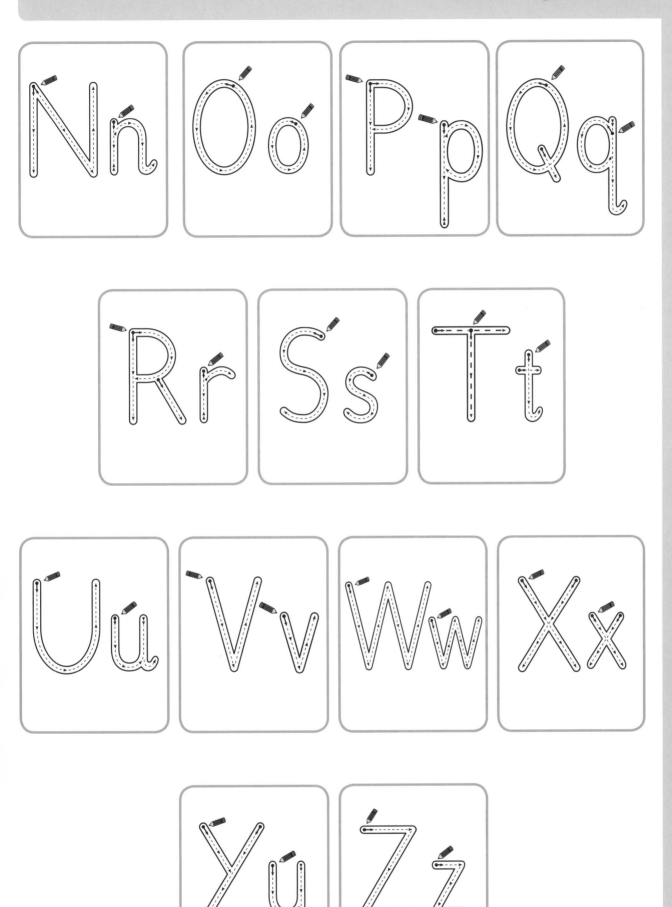

Words ending -ck

Read the words

Read the words. Write the words.

s → a → ck   s → o → ck   s → u → ck

_____   _____   _____

Make the words

Make some other words. Read the words.
Write the words.

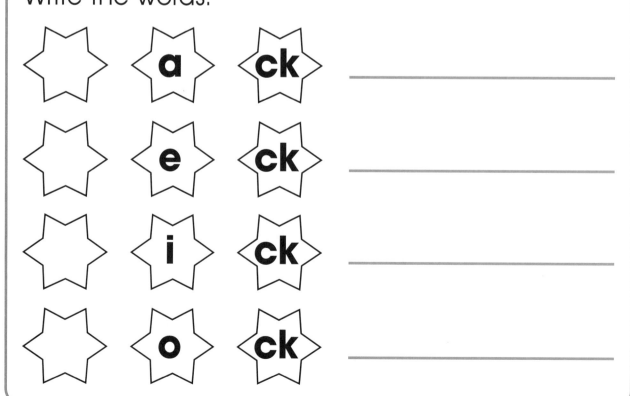

a   ck   _____

e   ck   _____

i   ck   _____

o   ck   _____

Read the words

Read the words. Write the words.

p → u → ff

_____

c → u → ff

_____

Read the rhyme

Huff and puff
Danny Duff

Write the words

Write some words
that end **ff**.
Use these letters:

o m u

_____

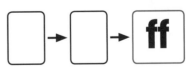

Read the words.

31

Words ending -ll

Read the rhymes

Circle **ll** in the rhymes.

Jack and Jill
went up the hill.

Ding, dong, dell,
Pussy's in the well.

Make the words

Make the words. Read the words. Write the words.

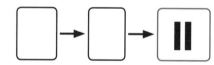
⬜ → ⬜ → **ll** _____

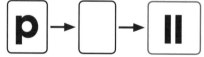
p → ⬜ → **ll** _____

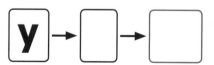
y → ⬜ → ⬜ _____

m → ⬜ → ⬜ _____

Read the words

Read the words. Write the words.

Read the rhyme

Hug and ki**ss**
Little Mi**ss** Bli**ss**

Write the words

Write some words that end **ss**.
Use these letters:
o b l e

☐ → ☐ → **ss**

☐ → ☐ → **ss**

Read the words.

Words beginning ch-

Say the word. Hear the sound.

chop

Write the letters.

Circle the ch- words

Circle the things that start **ch**. Say the words.

Parent's tip	You could play a game in which you make up (but do not write) sentences with 'ch'. For example: Chuck the chimp chooses cheese, Charlie chased a chicken, Cheryl chooses cherries.

Words beginning ch-

Make the words

Make some words. Read the words. Write the words.

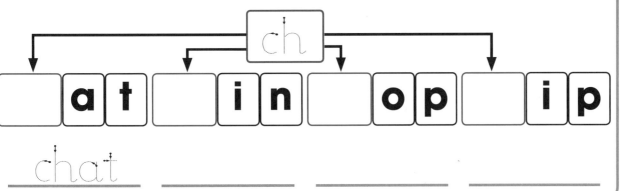

chat _____ _____ _____

Choose the words

Choose the correct word for each picture.
Write the word.

| chat or chin? | chop or chip? |

_____ _____

Make the words

Make some more words. Read the words. Write the
words.

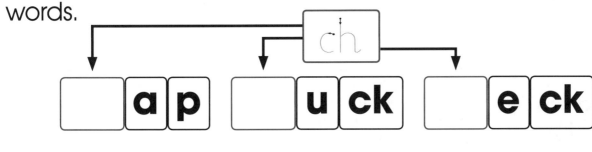

_____ _____ _____

Words beginning sh-

Say the word.
Hear the sound.

ship

Write the letters.

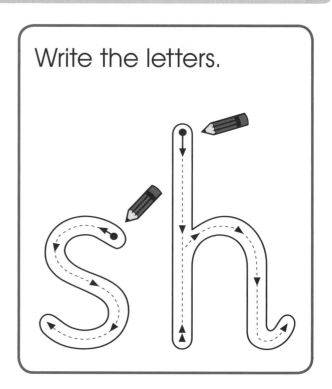

Circle the sh- words

Circle the things that start **sh**. Say the words.

Parent's tip

You could play a game in which you take turns to say what is in the sheep's shed. All words must begin with 'sh'. For example: in the sheep's shed is a ship, in the sheep's shed is a shoe....a shell... a sheet (and so on). To make it harder, try to repeat everything that has already been said.

36

Read the words

Read the words. Write the words.

| sh → i → p | sh → o → p | sh → e → d |

ship

Write the words

Write the word for each picture.

Make the words

Make some more words that start **sh**.

Read the words. Write the words.

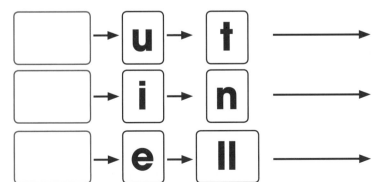

→ u → t	
→ i → n	
→ e → ll	

Words ending –sh

Read the words

Read the words. Write the words.

m → a → sh	h → u → sh	d → i → sh
m a s h		

Write the words

Write the word for each picture.

   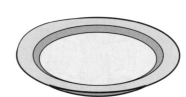   

_____   _____   _____

Make the words

Make some more words that end **sh**.

Read the words. Write the words.

w → i → ☐ ⟶ _____

b → a → ☐ ⟶ _____

p → o → ☐ ⟶ _____

Make the words

Add **sh** to complete each word.
Read the words.

____ip

ca ____

di ____

ma ____

fi ____

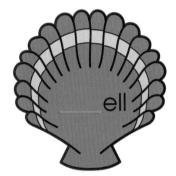
____ell

Write the words that begin **sh** in me.

Write the words that end **sh** in me.

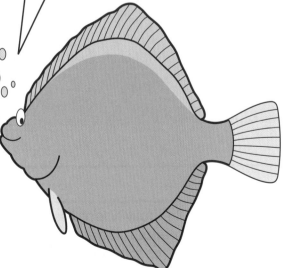

Words with th

Say the word.
Hear the sound.

bath

Write the letters.

Read the sentence

Circle **th** in the sentence.

This is Beth the moth on the path.

Parent's tip

This activity features letters and sounds your child has learned from previous pages. You could also encourage him/her to notice everyday words that begin or end with 'th'. Say the words, emphasising the 'th' sound. For example: Thursday, cloth, this, that, those, these, thing, thinking.

Make the words

Add **th** to complete each word. Read the words.

____in

____ick

ba____

mo____

pa____

Make the words

Make some more words with **th**.

Read the words. Write the words.

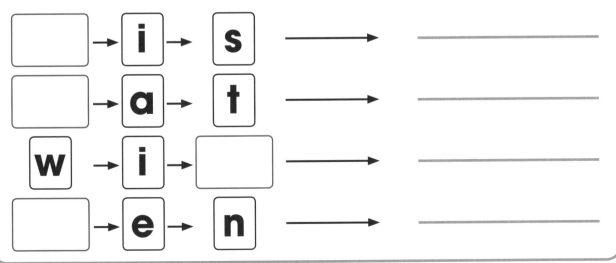

Words ending -ng

Read the words

Read the words. Write the words

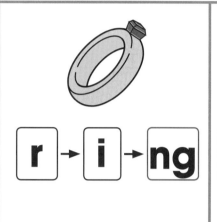

r → i → ng

k → i → ng

s → i → ng

_____ _____ _____

Read the rhyme

Circle **ng** in the rhyme.

Ding! Dong! Ding!
Ring, bells, ring.

Dong! Ding! Dong!
Sing a song.

Make the words

Add **ng** to complete each word.
Read the words.

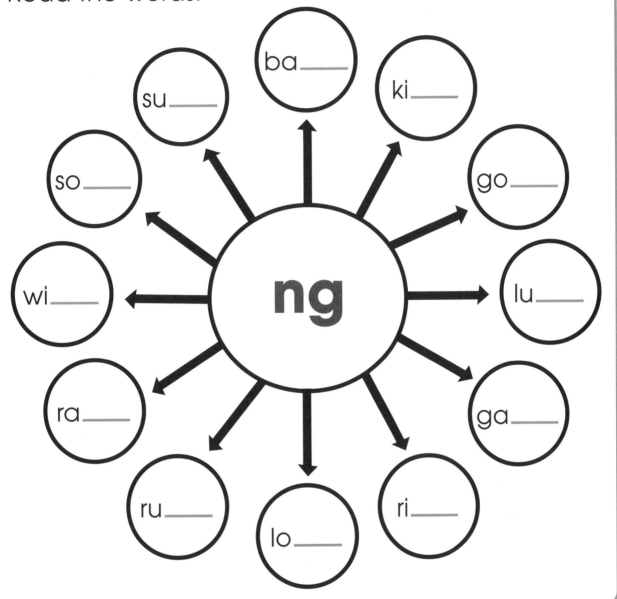

Parent's tip

The letters 'ng' represent a single sound and should not be 'sounded' separately. You could practise the sound with your child by making up silly songs (like the ones on p. 42). You could make up some 'ng' words, too!, For example:

Sing a song, it won't be long

Jango, Jango, do the tango

Ring bell ring; Ring for the king.

Letter j

Say the word.
Hear the sound.

jam

Write the letter.

Circle the j words

Circle the things that start **j**. Say the words.

Words starting j

Colour **j** on the ladder.

Say the words for the pictures.

Circle the things that start **j**.

A a
B b
C c
D d
E e
F f
G g
H h
I i
J j
K k
L l
M m
N n
O o
P p
Q q
R r
S s
T t
U u
V v
W w
X x
Y y
Z z

Letter v

Say the word.
Hear the sound.

van

Write the letter.

Circle the v words

Circle the things that start **v**. Say the words.

Words starting v

Colour **v** on the ladder.

Say the words for the pictures.
Circle the things that start **v**.

| A a |
| B b |
| C c |
| D d |
| E e |
| F f |
| G g |
| H h |
| I i |
| J j |
| K k |
| L l |
| M m |
| N n |
| O o |
| P p |
| Q q |
| R r |
| S s |
| T t |
| U u |
| V v |
| W w |
| X x |
| Y y |
| Z z |

Letter w

Say the word.
Hear the sound.

web

Write the letter.

Circle the w words

Circle the things that start **w**. Say the words.

Words starting w

Colour **w** on the ladder.

Say the words for the pictures.

Circle the things that start **w**.

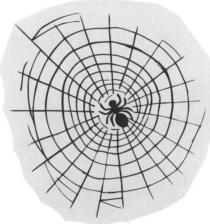

A a
B b
C c
D d
E e
F f
G g
H h
I i
J j
K k
L l
M m
N n
O o
P p
Q q
R r
S s
T t
U u
V v
W w
X x
Y y
Z z

Letter x

Say the word.
Hear the sound.

bo**x**

Write the letter.

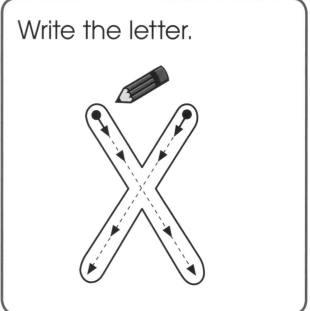

Circle the x words

Circle the things with **x** in them. Say the words.

Words with the letter x

Colour **x** on the ladder.

Say the words for the pictures.

Circle the things with **x** in them.

A a
B b
C c
D d
E e
F f
G g
H h
I i
J j
K k
L l
M m
N n
O o
P p
Q q
R r
S s
T t
U u
V v
W w
X x
Y y
Z z

Letter y

Say the word.
Hear the sound.

yak

Write the letter.

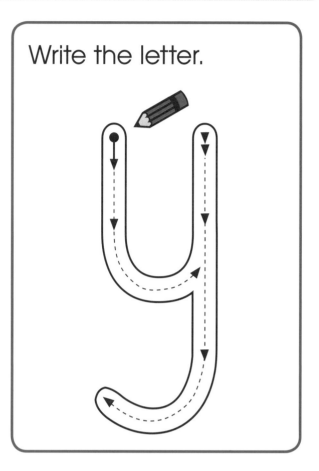

Circle the y words

Circle the things that start with **y**. Say the words.

Words starting y

Colour **y** on the ladder.

Circle the things that start **y**.

Say the words for the pictures.

A a	
B b	
C c	
D d	
E e	
F f	
G g	
H h	
I i	
J j	
K k	
L l	
M m	
N n	
O o	
P p	
Q q	
R r	
S s	
T t	
U u	
V v	
W w	
X x	
Y y	
Z z	

Words beginning z

Say the word.
Hear the sound.

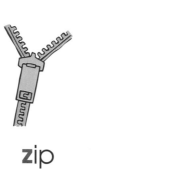

zip

Write the letter.

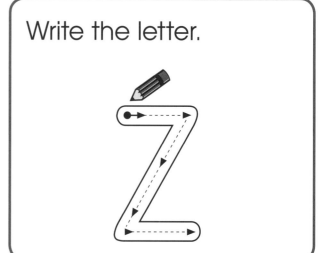

Circle the z words

Circle the things that start **z**. Say the words.

Make the words

Make some words that start **z**.
Read the words. Write the words.

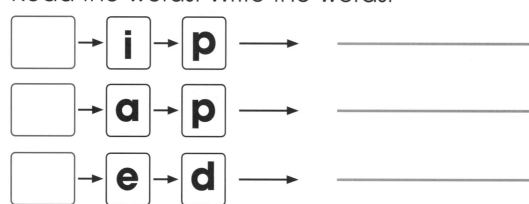

→ i → p →	_____
→ a → p →	_____
→ e → d →	_____

Words ending zz

Make words that end **zz**.

Read the words.

bu_____

fi_____

ja_____

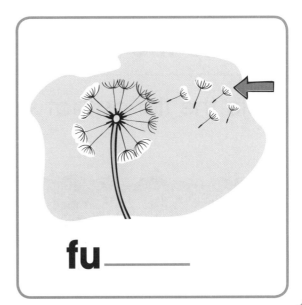

fu_____

Parent's tip

Before starting this page, practise the 'zz' sound with your child by saying 'buzz' with an emphasis on the 'zz'. You could use 'zz' words in 'silly' questions. For example: Do bees fizz? No, bees buzz; Do bees play jazz? No, bees just buzz; Do bees have fuzz? Yes, bees have fuzz, and they buzz.

Words beginning qu

Say the word.
Hear the sound.

queen

Write the letters.

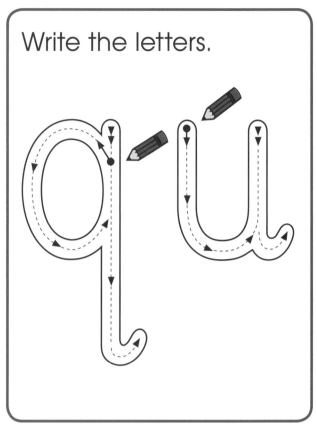

Circle the qu words

Circle the things that start **qu**. Say the words.

Quack!

Qu words

Say the words for the pictures.
Circle the things that start **qu**.

Make the words

Make some words that start **qu**.
Read the words. Write the words.

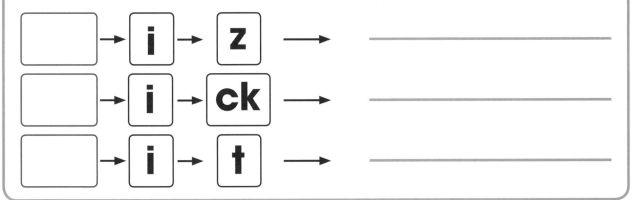

Alphabetical order

Activity 1

Join the letters to take the frog across the river.

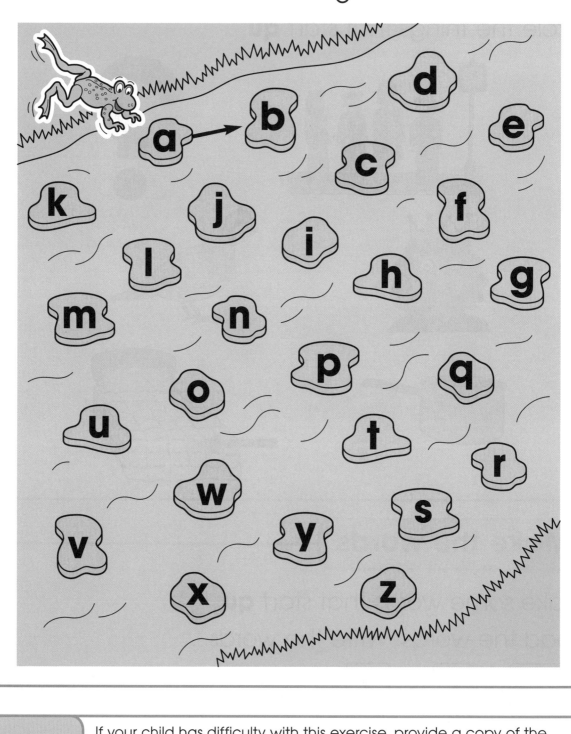

Parent's tip

If your child has difficulty with this exercise, provide a copy of the alphabet in lower-case letters so that he/she can check what comes next after 'landing' on each letter. After completing the page you could ask him/her to follow the frog's route and say the names of the letters. Children who find this easy might enjoy saying them in reverse order, or finding the letters before and after given letters. For example, 'Which letter comes after j?', 'Which letter comes before p?'

Activity 2

Join the letters to draw an animal.

Colour the animal.

Words with ee

Write the letters.

Make the words

Make the **ee** words.

Read the words. Write the words.

	→ l	→	_____
k	→	→ p	_____
b	→	→ f	_____
s	→	→ k	_____
f	→	→ l	_____
n	→	→ d	_____
ch	→	→ k	_____

r → ai → n

rain

Write the letters.

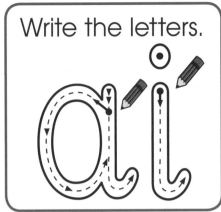

Circle the ai words

Circle the
things with **ai**.
Say the words.

Make the words

Make some **ai** words.
Read the words. Write the words.

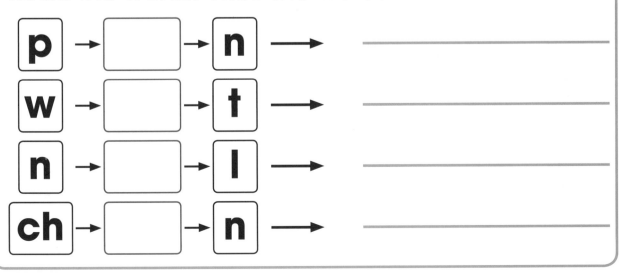

p → [ ] → n → _____

w → [ ] → t → _____

n → [ ] → l → _____

ch → [ ] → n → _____

Words with oo

Write the letters.

Make the words

Make the **oo** words.

Read the words. Write the words.

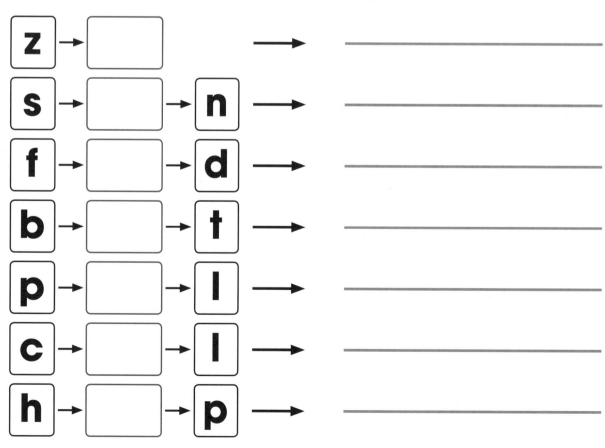

z	→	→	_____
s	→ n	→	_____
f	→ d	→	_____
b	→ t	→	_____
p	→ l	→	_____
c	→ l	→	_____
h	→ p	→	_____

Words with oa

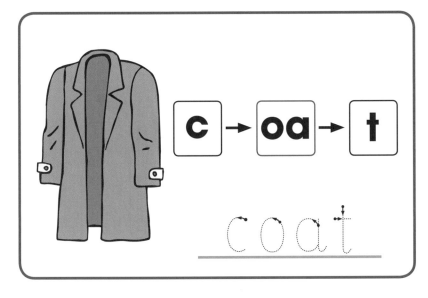

Write the letters.

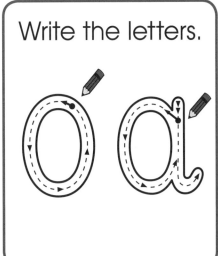

Make the words

Make the **oa** words.

Read the words. Write the words.

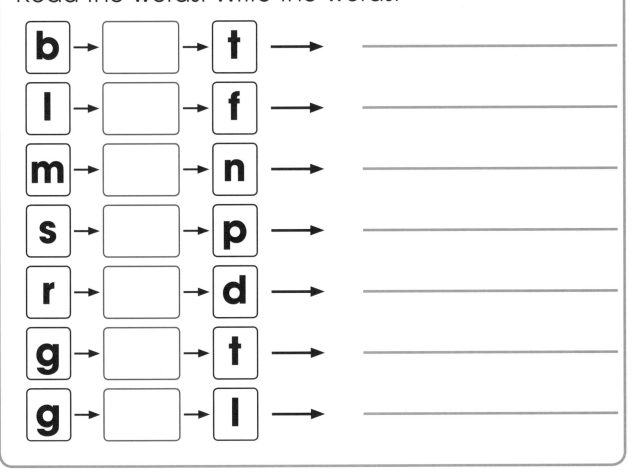

b → ⬚ → t → _____

l → ⬚ → f → _____

m → ⬚ → n → _____

s → ⬚ → p → _____

r → ⬚ → d → _____

g → ⬚ → t → _____

g → ⬚ → l → _____

Words with ar

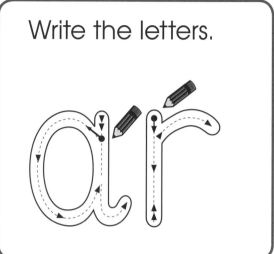

Write the letters.

Make the words

The dogs b [ ] k

in the p [ ] k.

The dogs b [ ] k at the

c [ ] in the d [ ] k.

Make the **ar** words.

Read the words. Write the words.

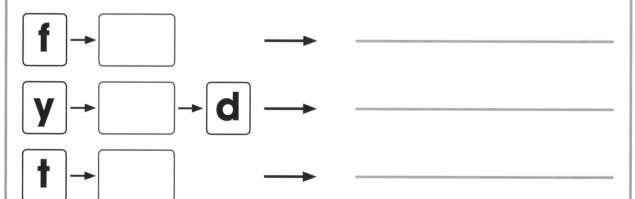

Make the words

Add **ar** to complete the words. Read the words.

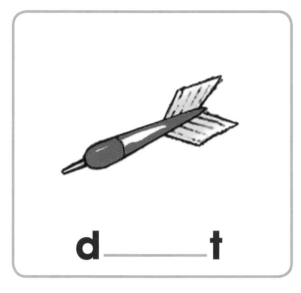

d____t

f____m

____k

____m

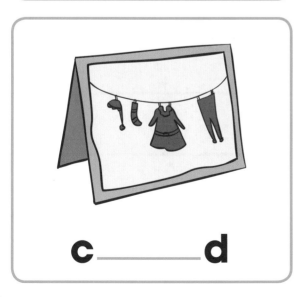

c____d

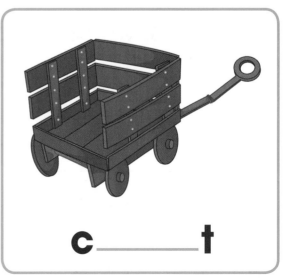

c____t

Words with or

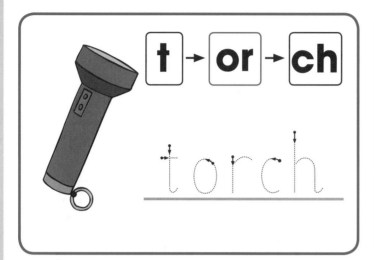

Write the letters.

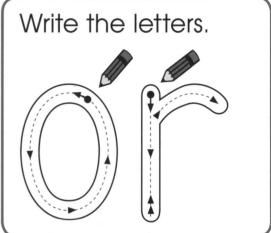

Circle the or words

Circle the things with **or**.
Say the words.

Make the words

Make the **or** words. Read the words. Write the words.

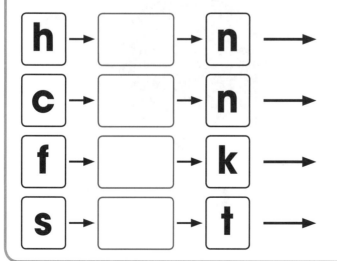

h	→		→	n	→	_____
c	→		→	n	→	_____
f	→		→	k	→	_____
s	→		→	t	→	_____

Make the words

Add **or** to complete the words. Read the words.

f___t

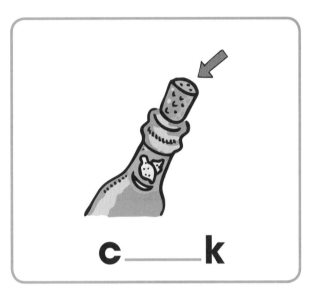

c___k

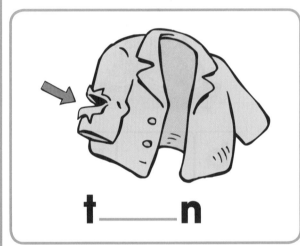

t___n

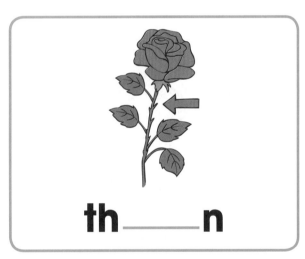

th___n

n___th

p___ch

Words with ur

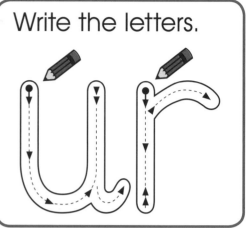

Write the letters.

Make the words

Make the **ur** words. Read the words. Write the words.

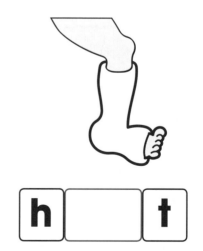

Make the words

Make the words with **ur**. Read the words.
Write the words.

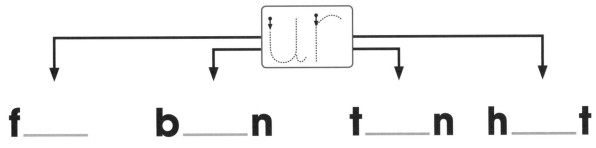

f___   b___n   t___n   h___t

f u r   _____   _____ _____

ch___n ch___ ch   s___f t___f

_____ _____ _____ _____

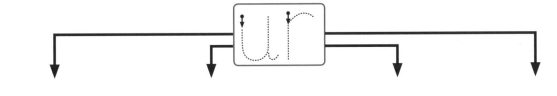

c___l T___kish f___nish t___nip

_____ _____ _____ _____

Words with ow

Write the letters.

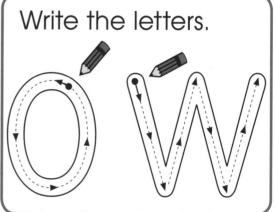

Make the words

Make the **ow** words. Read the words. Write the words.

___ l

t ___ n

b ___

g ___ n

Read the words

Read the words. Write the words.

c → ow

d → ow → n

h → ow → l

COW _____

_____

_____

Write the words

Write the word for each picture.

_____
_____
_____

Make the words

Make some words with **ow**.
Read the words. Write the words.

n → ☐ → _____

h → ☐ → _____

w → ☐ → _____

Words with oi

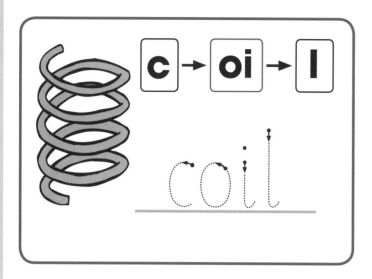

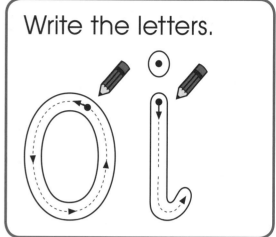

Write the letters.

Make the words

Make the **oi** words. Read the words. Write the words.

| | l |

| b | | l |

| c | | n |

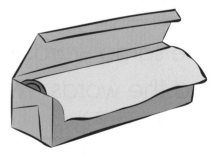

| f | | l |

Read the words

Read the words. Write the words.

j → oi → n	s → oi → l	qu → oi → t
	_____	_____

Write the words

Write the word for each picture.

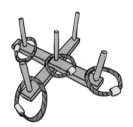  

_____   _____   _____

Make the words

Make some words with **oi**.
Read the words. Write the words.

[ ] → l → _____

c → [ ] → l → _____

b → [ ] → l → _____

Words with er

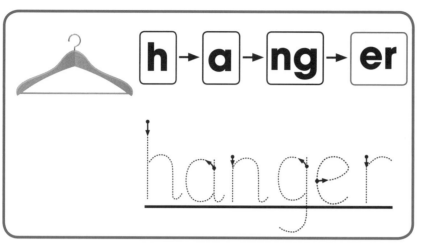

h → a → ng → er

hanger

Write the letters.

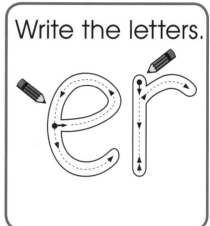

Make the words

Make the **er** words. Read the words. Write the words.

| b | oi | l | |

| r | o | ck | |

| p | ee | l | |

| f | ee | l | |

Read the words

Read the words. Write the words.

b → o → x → er	m → a → sh → er	b → u → zz → er
boxer		

Write the words

Write the word for each picture.

_____ _____ _____

Make the words

Make some words with **er**.

Read the words. Write the words.

sh → ow → ☐	→	_____
b → a → ng → ☐	→	_____
s → u → ff → ☐	→	_____

Words with ear

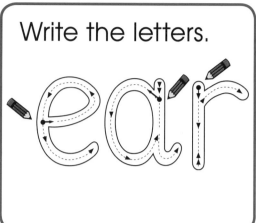

Write the letters.

Make the words

Make the **ear** words.

Read the words. Write the words.

t →

f →

d →

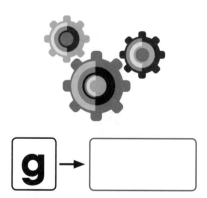

g →

Make the words

Make some words with **ear**. Read the words.
Write the words.

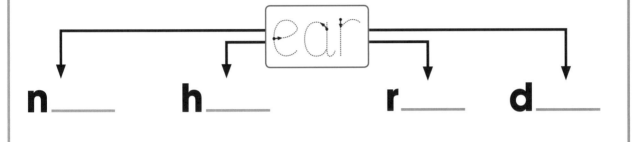

n____   **h**____   **r**____   **d**____

____   ____   ____   ____

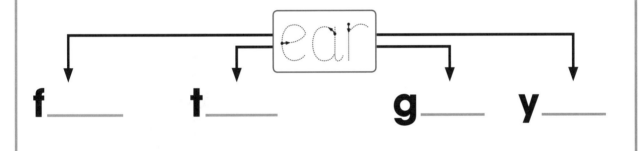

f____   **t**____   **g**____   **y**____

____   ____   ____   ____

g__ **box**   ____ **wig**   ____ **muff**

____   ____   ____

Words with air

ch → air

chair

Write the letters.

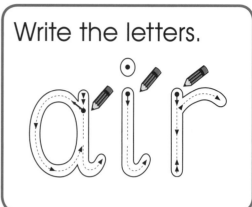

Make the words

Make the **air** words. Read the words.
Write the words.

f →

h →

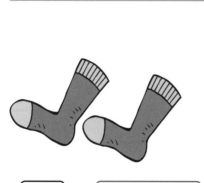

p →

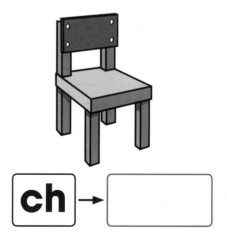

ch →

Dr Dure and his cure.

Write the letters.

Make the words

Make **ure** words.

Read the words. Write the words.

p → [ ] → _____

c → [ ] → _____

s → [ ] → _____

i → **n** → **s** → [ ] → _____

m → **a** → **n** → [ ] → _____

Words with igh

Write the letters.

Read the rhyme

Circle **igh** in the thyme.

Good night, sleep tight.
Wake up in the morning light
To do what is right with all your might.

Read the words

Read the words. Write the words.

h → igh	r → igh → t	l → igh → t
high	_____	_____

n → igh → t	f → igh → t	t → igh → t
_____	_____	_____

Write the words

Write the correct word under each picture.

_____

_____

_____

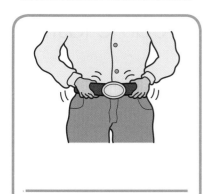

_____

_____

_____

Words with s + consonant t

Read the words

Read the words with **st**. Write the words.

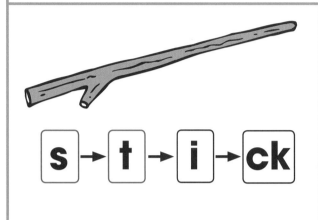

| s | → | t | → | i | → | ck |

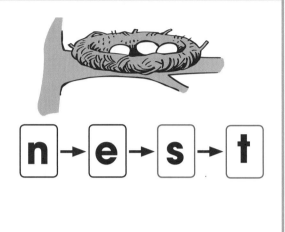

| n | → | e | → | s | → | t |

_____   _____

Read the sentences

Circle the words with **st**.

I did my best in the test.

I ran fast but still came last!

Write the words

Make some words. Read the words.

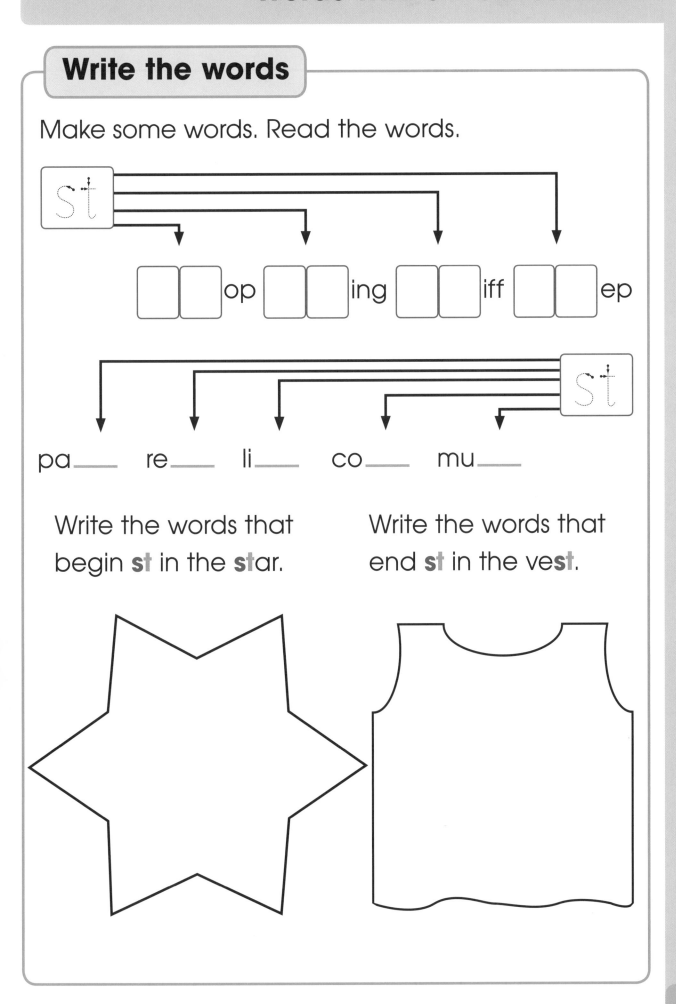

st

□□op   □□ing   □□iff   □□ep

pa___   re___   li___   co___   mu___

st

Write the words that begin **st** in the **st**ar.

Write the words that end **st** in the ve**st**.

Words beginning s + consonant

Read the words

Read the words. Write the words.

| s | → | n | → | i | → | ff |

_____

| s | → | w | → | i | → | ng |

_____

Write the letters

Write the missing letters. Read the words.

I can  **w i m**.

I can **k i p** .

I can **p i n** .

I can **n i p** .

Read the words

Read the words. Write the words.

| s | → | l | → | i | → | p |

_____

| s | → | t | → | i | → | ck |

_____

| s | → | p | → | e | → | ll |

_____

| s | → | m | → | a | → | sh |

_____

Make the words

Make another word. Read the word. Write the word.

| ☐ | → | k | → | i | → | n | → | _____

Words beginning consonant + l

Read the words

Read the words. Write the words.

b → l → a → ck

b → l → o → t

f → l → a → g → s

f → l → a → p

p → l → o → p

c → l → o → p

Read the words

Read the words. Write the words.

b → l → e → ss _____

b → l → o → b _____

c → l → i → ff _____

f → l → a → sh _____

Make the words

Complete the words. Read the words.
Write the words.

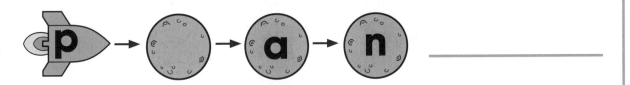

p → → a → n _____

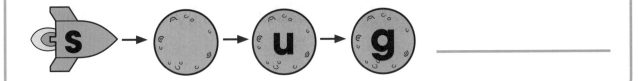

s → → u → g _____

Words beginning consonant + r

Read the words

Read the words. Write the words.

p → r → a → m

_____

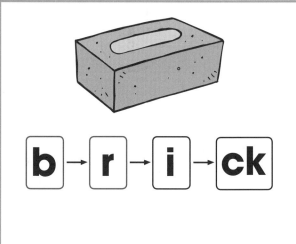

b → r → i → ck

_____

Talk about the picture

Who is **tr**amping over my **br**idge?

Let's eat the **gr**een **gr**ass.

trip! **tr**ap!
trip! **tr**ap!

the **tr**oll

the **thr**ee Billy Goats **Gr**uff

Words beginning consonant + r

Read the words

Read the words. Write the words.

b → r → i → ng _____

b → r → i → ck _____

c → r → a → ck _____

c → r → a → sh _____

Make the words

Complete the words. Read the words.
Write the words.

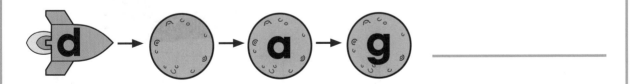

d → ( ) → a → g _____

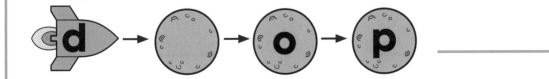

d → ( ) → o → p _____

Words ending l + consonant

Read the words

Read the words. Write the words.

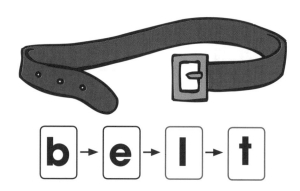

b → e → l → t

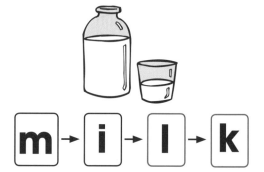

m → i → l → k

e → l → m

k → i → l → t

b → u → l → b

f → i → l → m

Make the words

Make the words. Read the words.

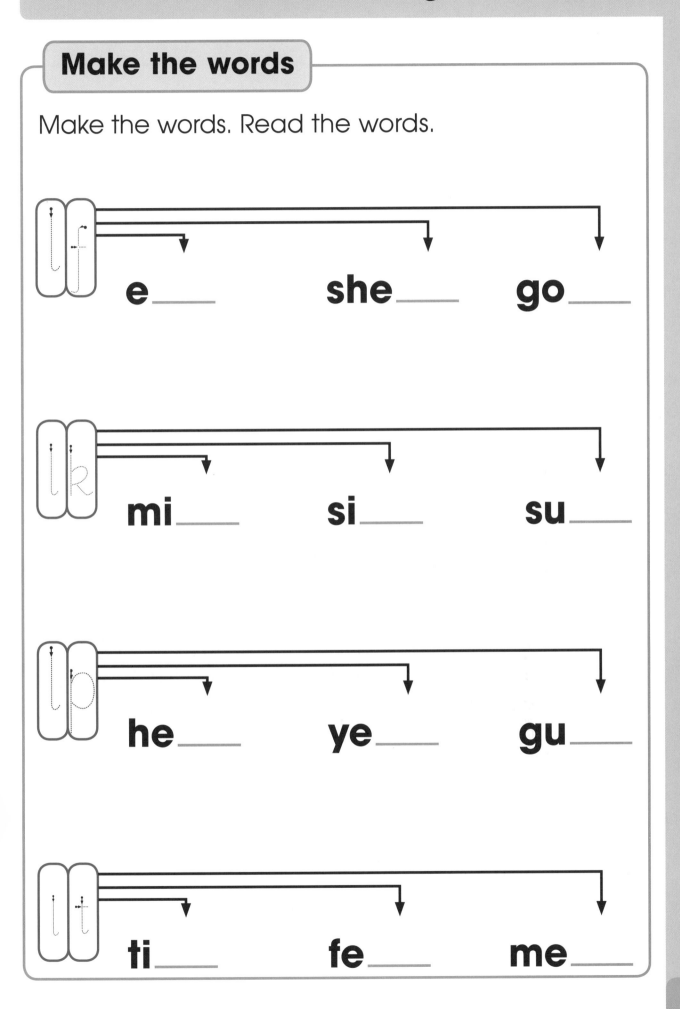

e_____   she_____   go_____

mi_____   si_____   su_____

he_____   ye_____   gu_____

ti_____   fe_____   me_____

Consonant blends

Words ending n + consonant

Read the words

Read the words. Write the words.

p → o → n → d

_____

t → e → n → t

_____

Read the rhyme

The ba**nd** is on the sa**nd**.

The sa**nd** is on the la**nd**.

Wave a ha**nd** to the ba**nd** on the sa**nd** –

on the la**nd**.

Isn't that gra**nd**? – A ba**nd** on the sa**nd**.

Read the words

Read the words. Write the words.

| p | → | o | → | n | → | d |

_____

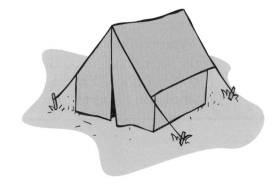

| t | → | e | → | n | → | t |

_____

| s | → | i | → | n | → | k |

_____

| h | → | a | → | n | → | d |

_____

Make the words

Make another word. Read the word. Write the word.

| | → | u | → | n | → | k | → | _____

What have I learned?

Note to parents

Present the tests one at a time. Explain that they will show what your child has learned. Some of the words have not appeared in the book but your child should be able to use what he/she has learned in order to complete them, i.e. to transfer learning from one example to another.

Explain to your child what to do. Use encouragement such as 'See if you can do this by yourself.' For correct answers, give praise such as 'Well done', 'You did well.' If incorrect, praise your child for having a try: 'It doesn't matter if you get things wrong. That's how we know what you need to practise.'

Test 1

Say the word for each picture.

Write the letter it starts with.

Test 2

Say the word for each picture.

Write the letter it starts with.

Test 3

Read the words.

mat	**ran**
den	**fig**
pot	**rug**

Test 4

Read the words.

back	**huff**
fell	**fuss**
buzz	**rag**

Test 5

Read the words and names.

chess	**shell**
chip	**bush**
than	**Beth**

Test 6

Read the words and names.

fang	**Jack**
vet	**web**
fix	**yap**

What have I learned?

Test 7

Read the words.

quiz	peel
zoom	toad
hard	fork

Test 8

Read the words.

charm	turn
vow	join
farmer	fear

Test 9

Read the words.

hair	pure
light	staff
vest	spear

Test 10

Read the words.

quill	blend
slush	clang
orbit	shelter